..............................., which piñata has the candy inside?

Shake the book really fast....

Come on, ...,
let's **POP** the balloons.

READY? SET? SMILE ...

Time for a funny birthday selfie,

....

HA, HA,
it's upside down!
Turn the book
.............................,
to see who's
monkeying
around.

Ready for your big present, ...?

Tilt the book this way....

HAPPY 3RD
BIRTHDAY

Happy 3rd Birthday

Now take a big
breath in and

BLOW

out your candles.

3, 2, 1 . . .

HAPPY BIRTHDAY

HAPPY BIRTHDAY TO YOU,
HAPPY BIRTHDAY TO YOU,
HAPPY BIRTHDAY, DEAR
....
HAPPY BIRTHDAY
TO YOU!

The funniest thing I did on my **3rd** birthday was ....
....
....

MY MOST AWESOME
PRESENT IS:

MY FAVORITE PARTY GAME IS:

HAPPY BIRTHDAY

My yummy cake

MY AMAZING PARTY GUESTS ARE:

HAPPY 3RD BIRTHDAY

Illustrated by Hazel Quintanilla
Designed by Nicky Scott

Copyright © Orangutan Books Ltd 2020

Published by Sourcebooks Wonderland,
an imprint of Sourcebooks Kids
P.O. Box 4410, Naperville, Illinois 60567-4410
(630) 961-3900
sourcebookskids.com

Source of Production: Amazon Printing
Date of Production: March 2020
Run Number: POD
Printed and bound in the United States of America.
AMZ

Made in the USA
Monee, IL
15 September 2021

78125012R00019